STEVIE WONDER

Arranged for Piano / Vocal / Guitar 1985 5

Exclusive Distributors:
Music Sales Limited, 8/9 Frith Street, London W1V 5TZ, England.
Music Sales Pty Limited, 120 Rothschild Avenue, Rosebery, NSW 2018, Australia.

This book © Copyright 1985, 1988 & 1991 by Wise Publications.
Order No. AM 60591 ISBN 0.7119.0761.7

Designed by Michael Bell Design. Typeset by Capital Setters Limited. Photographs courtesy of London Features International.

Music Sales' complete catalogue lists thousands of titles and is free from your local music shop, or direct from Music Sales Limited.
Please send a cheque/postal order for £1.50 for postage to: Music Sales Limited, Newmarket Road, Bury St. Edmunds, Suffolk IP33 3YB.

Your Guarantee of Quality:
As publishers, we strive to produce every book to the highest commercial standards.
The book has been carefully designed to minimise awkward page turns and to make playing from it a real pleasure.
Particular care has been given to specifying acid-free, neutral-sized paper which has not been chlorine bleached but produced with special regard for the environment.
Throughout, the printing and binding have been planned to ensure a sturdy, attractive publication which should give years of enjoyment.
If your copy fails to meet our high standards, please inform us and we will gladly replace it.

Printed in the United Kingdom by J.B. Offset Printers (Marks Tey) Limited, Marks Tey, Essex.

WISE PUBLICATIONS
LONDON / NEW YORK / SYDNEY

COMPLETE

I JUST CALLED TO SAY I LOVE YOU

Moderately ♩ = 112

Words and Music by
STEVIE WONDER

1. No New Year's Day   to cel - e -
   rain;   no flow - ers

brate;   no choc - 'late cov - ered can - dy hearts
bloom;   no wed - ding Sat - ur - day ___ with - in ___

I love_____ you.____ And I mean _

___ it from__ the bot - tom of __ my ____ heart.

3. No sum - mer's heart.   I just called __

heart,   of my   heart,   of my

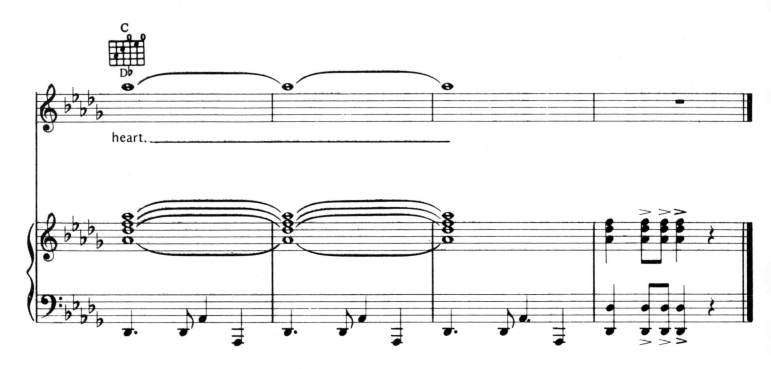

heart.

Verse 3:

No summer's high; no warm July;
No harvest moon to light one tender August night.
No autumn breeze; no falling leaves;
Not even time for birds to fly to southern skies.

Verse 4:

No Libra sun; no Halloween;
No giving thanks to all the Christmas joy you bring.
But what it is, though old so new
To fill your heart like no three words could ever do.

(To Chorus:)

HAPPY BIRTHDAY

Words and Music by
STEVIE WONDER

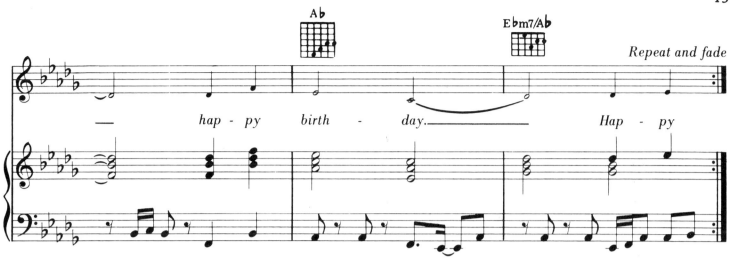

Repeat and fade

hap - py   birth - day._____   Hap - py

2nd Verse:

I just never understood
How a man who died for good
Could not have a day that would
Be set aside for his recognition.
Because it should never be,
Just because some cannot see
The dream as clear as he,
That they should make it become an illusion.
And we all know everything
That he stood for time will bring.
For in peace our hearts will sing
Thanks to Martin Luther King.
Happy birthday....

3rd Verse:

The time is overdue
For people like me and you
Who know the way to truth
Is love and unity to all God's children.
It should be a great event,
And the whole day should be spent
In full remembrance
Of those who lived and died
For the oneness of all people.
So let us all begin.
We know that love can win.
Let it out, don't hold it in.
Sing as loud as you can.
Happy birthday...

Recitation
For fade
Ending

We know the key to unity of all people.
It was in the dream that we had so long ago,
That lives in all of the hearts of people
That believe in unity. We will make the
Dream become a reality. I know we will,
Because our hearts tell us so.

LOVE LIGHT IN FLIGHT

Words and Music by
STEVIE WONDER

Chorus 2:
Make me feel like paradise; fill me with your kisses.
Make the moment feel just right; take me up and away.
'Cause I have waited all my life, for the one worth giving,
And I don't have to think it twice, let's go up and away!

Verse 2:
We need just to feel it to know that our lovin' has the power,
Showing that these feelings emanate from you and me.
With love high aviation, we will fly forever and one hour,
Giving us the always to live out all our fantasies.

THAT GIRL

Words and Music by
STEVIE WONDER

1. That girl thinks that she's so fine,— that soon she'll have my mind.—
2. That girl thinks that she's so bad,— she'll change my tears to joy from sad.—
3. (Instrumental ad lib)
4. (See additional lyrics)

That girl thinks that she's so smart,—
She says she keeps the up-per hand—

Verse 4: That girl knows every single man would ask her for her hand;
But she says her love is much too deep for them to understand.
She says her love has been crying out, but her lover hasn't heard;
But what she doesn't realize is that I've listened to every word.
That's why I know I'll tell her that I love her.

THE WOMAN IN RED

Words and Music by
STEVIE WONDER

1. Am I see - ing what I think I see,
2. *See additional lyrics*

or are my eyes play - ing tricks on me?

Verse 2:
M-m-m-miss, please pardon me;
Now listen to me, I can hardly speak.
I haven't been this much confused
Since daddy caught me trying on his shoes.
Now I'm too old to be acting like this,
But there's something about her I just can't resist.
My heart is beating like a big bass drum,
And my mind is saying, that girl's the one.

(To Chorus:)

ALL I DO

Words and Music by
STEVIE WONDER,
CLARENCE PAUL and
MORRIS BROADNAX

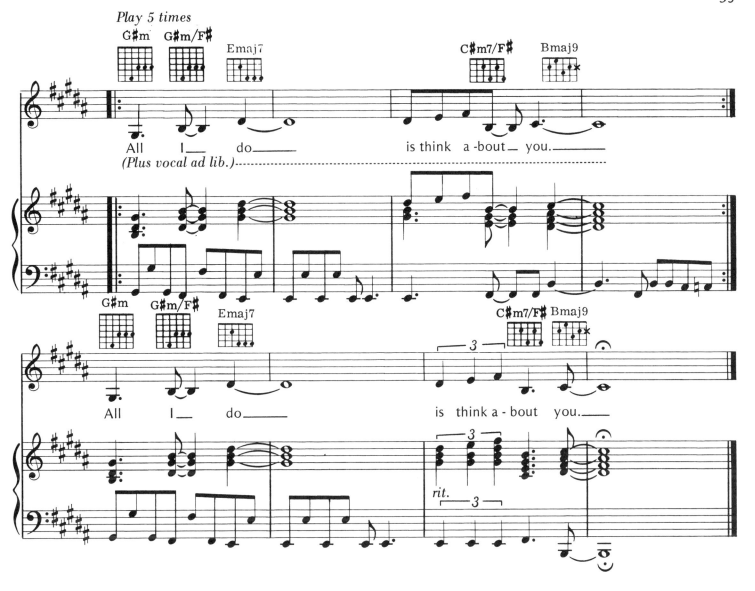

2nd Verse: Think of how exciting it would be
If you should discover you feel like me.
If you should discover this dream is for two,
Well, I'm gonna tell you, girl. . .
I'd light a candle every day,
And pray that you'll always feel this way,
And pray that our love will forever be new.
'Cause all I do is think about you.
All I do is think about you.
All I do is think about you.

Instrumental

Well, let me tell you girl...

3rd Verse: I'd light a candle every day,
And pray that you'll always feel this way,
And pray that our love will forever be new.
I'm gonna tell you, girl. . .
If I cannot have you for my own,
I'd rather be lonely and all alone.
I'd rather keep thinking the way that I do,
'Cause all I do is think about you.
All I do is think about you.
All I do is think about you.

LATELY

Moderately Slow

Words and Music by
STEVIE WONDER

mean good - bye.

2nd Verse: Lately I've been staring in the mirror,
Very slowly picking me apart;
Trying to tell myself I have no reason
With your heart.
Just the other night while you were sleeping,
I vaguely heard you whisper someone's name.
But when I ask you of the thoughts you're keeping,
You just say nothing's changed.
Well, I'm a man........etc.

WEAKNESS

Words and Music by
STEVIE WONDER

Moderately, with a swing

1. Ev - 'ry time I think our love is drift - ing __ a -
2. Ev - 'ry time I think your love has no __ more __ to

part, ___
give, ___

some - thing al - ways throws it back to - me
you do some - thing more to take me

MOMENTS AREN'T MOMENTS

Gently (♩ = 76)

Words and Music by
STEVIE WONDER

Verse:

1. Ten - der, warm and _ se - rene are the words that might come close to _ hav - ing rem - nants of the feel - ings that we _ can no long - er hide.

Verse 2:
Gentle, quiet, so soft are the wings of love
That can send us off to an ever
Splendor, unknown to all in our time.
Trusting in the unknown and giving into what
Feelings have shown will take us to altered
Intimacies in our lives, where we will find that . . .

(To Chorus:)

DID I HEAR YOU SAY YOU LOVE ME

Moderately

Words and Music by
STEVIE WONDER

2nd Verse: Did I hear you say you need me?
Well, baby tell me the truth,
'Cause if you **really, really need me**
My **sweetness**, here's what I'll do:
Cut out all my crazy playing,
'Cause for your love I have been laying.
Just tell me that is what you're saying,
And I'll be yours without delaying.
I've been standing...

3rd Verse: Did I hear you say you want me?
Now please don't give me no mess,
'Cause if you **really, really need me**,
You've got to give me your best.
Put my love life right in pocket
And dare someone to try to top it.
And when you think I want to drop it
Just love me till I beg, "Don't stop it."
'Cause I've been standing...

CASH IN YOUR FACE

Words and Music by
STEVIE WONDER

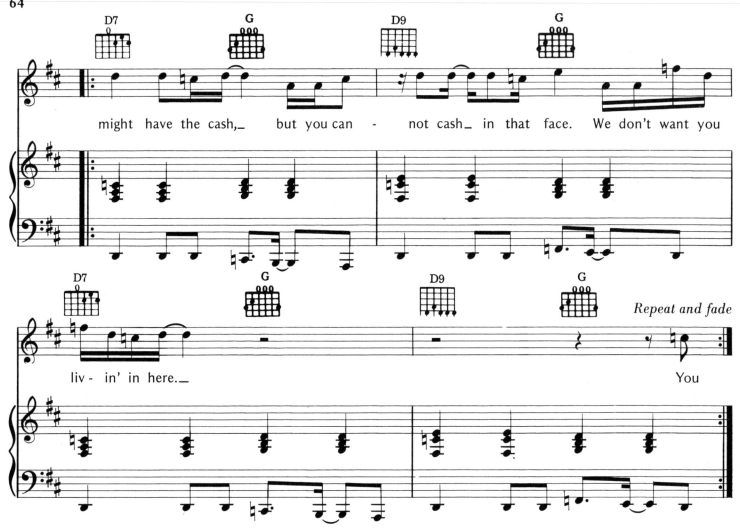

might have the cash,_ but you can - not cash_ in that face. We don't want you

liv - in' in here._

Repeat and fade

You

2nd Verse:
I graduated from Howard U.
My job is paying good money, too.
And, if you check on my resumé,
You'll find they all wanted me to stay.
Well, I can't take the time out
To check your credit card,
'Cause the computer just broke down today.
Well, I'll stop by here tomorrow
To complete our interview,
But I know what you're gonna say;
I know what your bottom line is.
You might have the cash....

3rd Verse:
Our first child is due here any day;
That's why we're desperate for a place to stay.
The location is so perfect too,
So please try to do what you can do.
Well, in this apartment complex
No children are allowed,
And if you told me that
I could have saved you a lot of time.
Well, I thought the bill was passed
That said you could not discriminate,
But I know some excuse you'll find,
Because your bottom line is...
You might have the cash...

AS IF YOU READ MY MIND

Words and Music by
STEVIE WONDER

you touched_ my soul._ As if you knew ex -act - ly

where I want -ed to go._ As if

Repeat and Fade

2nd Verse: Take a chance on the secret
That you hide far beneath your dreams.
Use your wildest imagination.
You just tell me what it is,
And I will make it be.

3rd Verse: Let's get high on the happy
With a toast to you and me.
Love is here just for the giving,
And between us we've got all the love
We'll ever need.

DO LIKE YOU

Words and Music by
STEVIE WONDER

Show___ me how___ to___

do like___ you._____

To Coda ⊕ N.C.

D.S. al Coda

3. Once at

Coda

2nd Verse: Late at night when he was supposed to be sleeping,
              You could hear the pitter patter of feet creeping
              To where music would play.
              To his sister he would say,
              Before his father said, "Hey boy,
              Get right back in that **bed.**"
              Show me...

3rd Verse: Once at school they put on a talent contest
              To find out who could really boogie the best.
              But his mama said, "No,
              Keita's much too young **to go.**"
              But his sister said, "Please, let him go
              So the world can see."

4th Verse: When they saw him they said he must be crazy.
              "Look at him, he ain't nothing but a baby."
              But soon as he began
              You knew the contest he would **win,**
              Because everyone in the audience
              Began to cheer.
              Show me...

FRONT LINE

Words and Music by
STEVIE WONDER

At six-teen I just____ had to be a man at an-y cost.

I vol-un-tee red for____ Vi - et - nam____ where I got my leg____ shot off.

I re-call a quote____ from a mov - ie that said,____ "Who's more a man____

than a man with a rea - son that's worth dy - in' for?"

an - oth - er war_____ is in the brew - ing;
but what a - bout_____ the lives_____ of yes - ter - day_____ and the man-
- y hap - py fam - i - lies_____ that have been_____ ru - ined?

Verse 2:
They gave me a uniform and a tiny salty pill
To stop a big urge I might have for the wrong kind of thrill.
They put a gun in my hand and said, "Shoot until he's dead."
But it's hard to kill when "please, I'm your friend" echoes through your head.
Brought up in church, taught no man should take another's life
But then put in a jungle where life has no price.
(To Chorus:)

Verse 3:
My niece is a hooker and my nephew's a junkie too.
But they say I have no right to tell them how they should do.
They laugh and say "quit braggin' 'bout the war you shoulda never been in."
But my mind is so brainwashed I'd prob'ly go back and do it again.
I walk the neighborhood paradin' my purple heart
With a fear of agent orange that no one will stop.
(To Chorus:)

IT'S YOU

Words and Music by
STEVIE WONDER

1. I look in-side my
2. I look be-hind, and

crys - tal ball of de - sire,
what a sight is the mire.

ROCKET LOVE

Words and Music by
STEVIE WONDER

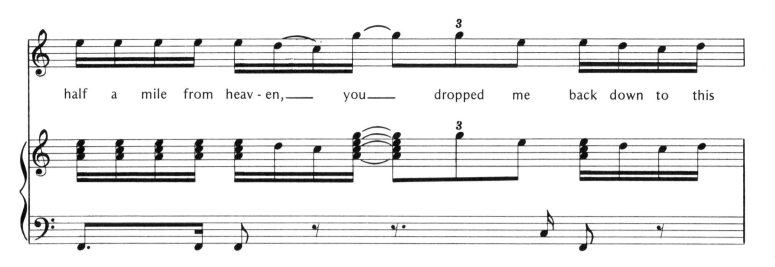

half a mile from heav-en,___ you___ dropped me back down to this

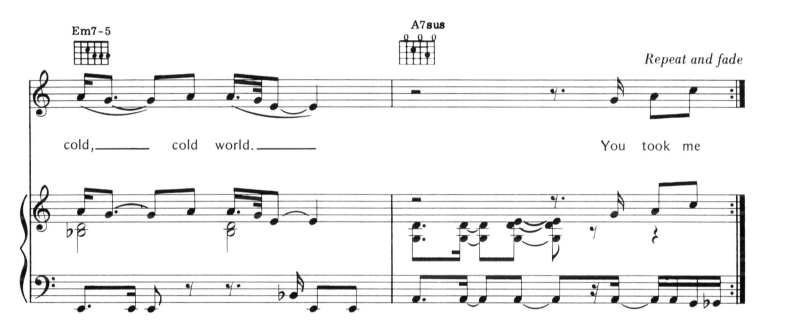

Em7-5   A7sus   *Repeat and fade*

cold,___ cold world.___   You took me

2nd Verse: A female Shakespeare of your time
With looks to blow Picasso's mind,
You were the best.
Your body moved with grace and song
Like symphonies by Bach or Brahms,
Nevertheless. Oh, oh,
You took me...

RIBBON IN THE SKY

Words and Music by
STEVIE WONDER

(Instrumental ad lib)

There's a

rib - bon in the sky for our love. _____

rit.

I AIN'T GONNA STAND FOR IT

Words and Music by
STEVIE WONDER

1. Don't wan-na be - lieve what they're tell - in' me;
2. (See additional lyrics)

that some - bod-y's been pick - in' in my cher - ry

tree. _____ Don't wan-na mis -

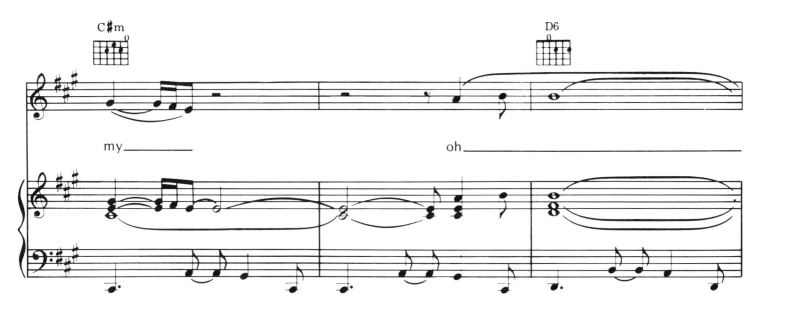

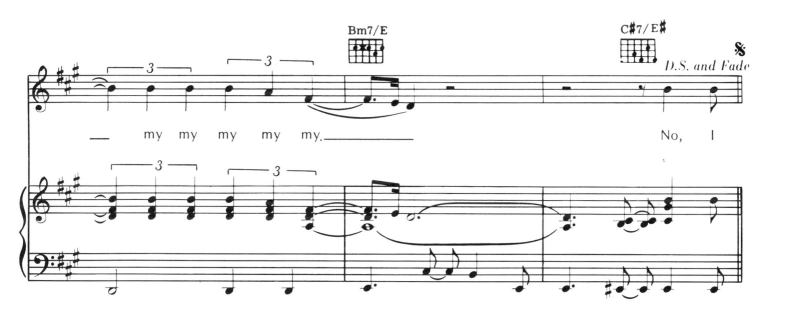

2nd Verse: Don't wanna believe what somebody said,
But somebody said somebody's shoes was under my bed.
Don't wanna 'cause nobody no bodily harm,
But somebody's been rubbin' on my good luck charm.
And I ain't gonna stand...

DO I DO

Words and Music by
STEVIE WONDER

1.When ___ I see ___ you on ___ the street, ___ my ___ whole bod-
2.3.4. (see additional lyrics)

- y ___ gets weak. ___ When ___ you're stand-

Verse 2:
When I hear you on the phone,
Your sweet sexy voice turns my ear all the way on.
Just the mention of your name
Seems to drive my head insane.
Girl, do I do ...etc.

Verse 3:
From the time that I awake
I'm imagining the good love that we'll make.
If to me your vibe can do all this
Just imagine how it's gonna feel when we hug and kiss.
Sugar, do I do ...etc.

Verse 4:
I don't care how long it might take,
'Cause I know the woman for me — you I'll make.
'Cause I will not deny myself the chance
Of being part of what feels like the right romance.
Girl, do I do ...etc.

MASTER BLASTER
(JJammin')

Words and Music by
STEVIE WONDER

jam-min', and jam-min', and jam-min', jam on.

jam - min', jam-min', jam-min', jam- min'

on.

D.C.

Verse 4:
From the park I hear rhythms;
Marley's hot on the box;
Tonight there will be a party
On the corner, at the end of the block.
Didn't know ... *(To Chorus:)*

Verse 5:
They want us to join their fighting,
But our answer today
Is to let all our worries,
Like the breeze, through our fingers, slip away.

Verse 6:
Peace has come to Zimbabwe;
Third world's right on the one;
Now's the time for celebration,
'Cause we've only just begun.
Didn't know ... *(To Chorus:)*

Verse 7:
You ask me am I happy;
Well, as matter of fact,
I can say that I'm ecstatic,
'Cause we all just made a pact.

Verse 8:
We've agreed to get together;
Joined as children in Jah.
When you're moving in the positive,
Your destination is the brightest star.
Didn't know ... *(To Chorus:)*

Chorus: (vocal ad lib)
Oh, oh, oh, oh, oh, you
(We're in the middle of the makin's
Of the master blaster jammin').
Would be jammin' until the break of dawn.
Don't you stop the music, oh no.
(We're in the middle of the makin's
Of the master blaster jammin').
(Repeat background)
Oh, oh, oh, you
(We're in the middle of the makin's
Of the master blaster jammin').
Would be jammin' until the break of dawn.
I bet you if someone approached you yesterday
To tell you that you would be jammin'
You would not believe it because
You never thought that you would be jammin'.
Oh, oh, oh, oh,
(We're in the middle of the makin's
Of the master blaster jammin').
Jammin' til the break of dawn.
Oh, oh, oh, you may as well believe
What you're feeling because you feel your body jammin'.
Oh, oh, you would be jammin' until the break of dawn.
(We're in the middle of the makin's
Of the master blaster jammin').
(Repeat background)

DON'T DRIVE DRUNK

Words and Music by
STEVIE WONDER

1. He and his wife ___ have had *prob - lems* that
2.3. *See additional lyrics*

picks out that bot - tle of gin. _____

Drinks like there's no *to - mor - row,* and de - cides _____

_____ to take a spin. _____ Oh. _____

Chorus: Don't drive ____ *drunk.* ____ Don't drive ____ drunk.

No,___ don't drive ___ *drunk.* ___ Moth - ers

a - gainst drunk driv - ers are mad. ___

Verse 2:
Teenager at a live party
Says, "Give me one for the road."
But he's already so inebriated,
If you lit a smoke he'd explode.
Oh, but bartender says, "I don't think so."
Young one says, "I can deal."
Staggering, he says, "Check y'all later."
But I really don't think he will.

(To Chorus:)

Verse 3:
Boy out with girl on their first date
Gets pulled over by the law.
Officer says, "Hey, can't you drive straight?
Or have you been drinking alcohol?"
Boy says, "Man, are you crazy?"
Cop says, "Hey, then walk this line."
But results from the breathalizer
Proves he's charged with D.U.I.

(To Chorus:)

WE CAN WORK IT OUT

Words and Music by
JOHN LENNON and PAUL McCARTNEY

We can work it out,— we can work it out.— Life is ve-ry short,_ and there's no time_

_____ for fuss-ing and fight-ing, my friend.

I have al-ways thought_ that it's a crime,_____ so I will

D.%. al Coda   ⊕ *CODA*

ask you once a - gain.

Checklist of important piano books.

The books below are available from your local music shop who will order them for you if not in stock.

If there is no music shop near you, you may order direct from Music Sales Limited (Dept. M), 8/9 Frith Street, London, W1V 5TZ. Please always include 85p to cover post/packing costs.

A Start At The Piano
AM 40650

Alison Bell's Graded For Piano Pieces Book 1: Very Easy
AM 30297

Book 5: Upper Intermediate
AM 30339

Anthology Of Piano Music Volume 1: Baroque
AM 10968

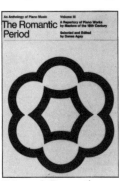

Volume 3: Romantic
AM 10984

Barrelhouse And Boogie Piano
OK 64659

Big Note Piano Book 1
AM 28226

Bud Powell: Jazz Masters Series
AM 23219

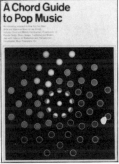

Chord Guide To Pop Music
AM 10596

The Classic Piano Repertoire Bach
EW 50023

Chopin
EW 50015

Promenade Theory Papers Book 1
PB 40583

Classics To Moderns Book 1
YK 20014

Classics To Moderns Sonatas & Sonatinas
YK 20204

Themes & Variations
YK 20196

More Classics To Moderns Book 1
YK 20121

Dave Brubeck: Jazz Masters Series
AM 21189

Easy Classical Piano Duets
AM 31949

The Complete Piano Player By Kenneth Baker Book 1
AM 34828

Book 2
AM 34836

Book 3
AM 34844

Book 4
AM 34851

Book 5
AM 34869

Style Book
AM 35338

Improvising Rock Piano
AM 22039

Easy Piano Solos
Simple Arrangements
of Pop Classics
AM 28648

**For Your Eyes Only & 18
Movie Themes**
AM 36609

**Genius Of George
Shearing**
AM 25990

Genius Of Art Tatum
BG 10085

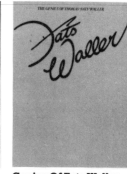

Genius Of Fats Waller
AM 24423

Genius of Andre Previn
AM 25982

**Genius Of Jazz Giants
Volume 1**
AM 36708

Jazz Hanon
AM 27418

Blues Hanon
AM 27889

Boogie Woogie Hanon
AM 27400

**Home Piano Library
Classics**
AM 34141

Rock 'n' Roll
AM 36922

Showmusic
AM 36724

Hooked On Classics
AM 32210

How To Play Blues Piano
AM 35197

**How To Play Boogie-
Woogie**
AM 33317

Improvising Rock Piano
AM 22039

Ballet Music
AM 32939

Beatles
NO 17907

Rock and Roll
AM 19556

Elvis
AM 20868

Familiar Songs
AM 36419

Paul Simon
PS 10214

Christmas Songs
AM 22641

Walt Disney
WD 10260

Jazz Riffs For Piano
AM 21502

**The Joy Of
Bach**
YK 21004

Boogie and Blues
YK 21020

Christmas
YK 21194

Folk Songs
YK 21061

Mozart
YK 21244

Piano Entertainment
YK 21178

Romantic Piano: Book 1
YJK 21145

First Year Piano
YK 21053

Piano Duets
YK 21111

Pianist's Picture Chords
AM 21429

The Piano Chord Finder
AM 24860

More Piano Pieces For Children
YK 20220

The Music Of Michel Legrand
AM 25727

Piano Adventures Pop Blends
AM 32079

I Love Pop
AM 32087

Popular Piano Solos Book 1
AM 24100

Book 7: Blues
AM 33879

Book 8: Jazz
AM 33861

Easy Classical Piano Duets
AM 31949

Easy Folk Piano Duets
AM 31956

Ragtime: 100 Authentic Rags
AM 25081

Rock Keyboard Styles
(with cassette)
DG 20017

The Best Of McCartney Easy Piano
MY 70101

Songs Of World War II
AM 14226

Teach Yourself Rock Piano
AM 25172

Teaching Piano (Combined) By Denes Agay.
YK 20279

Thelonious Monk: Jazz Masters Series
AM 19423

They All Played Ragtime
OK 61572

Timeless Standards
AM 36641

Timeless Country Standards
AM 36658

Timeless Jazz Standards
AM 36666

Tomorrow: 18 Broadway Blockbusters
AM 36617

With My Love
AM 25925